Published in the UK by
POWERFRESH Limited
3 Gray Street
Northampton
NN1 3QQ

Telephone 01604 630 996
Facsimile 01604 621 013
E Mail   pwrfresh@nccnet.co.uk

ISBN 1 874125 988

Printed in the UK by Avalon Print Northampton
Powerfresh October 1999

SPORT FOR THE ELDERLY

BY THE
SILVEY JEX PARTNERSHIP

BANG!

....It's no use, he can't go on....he's asleep.

Oh bad luck Norman.

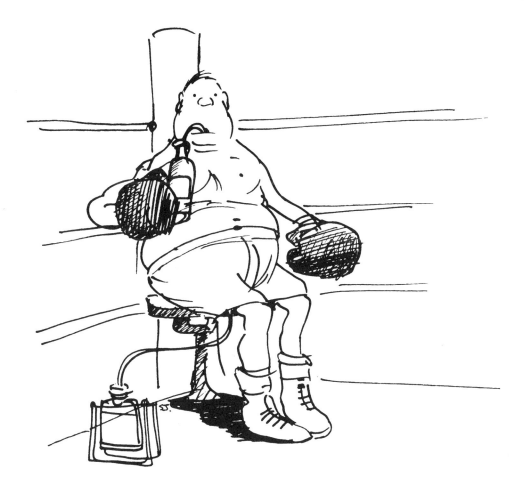

BOY LOOK AT THE TITS ON THAT!

...46...47...48...49......

On your marks....get set .....throw

AND THE RESULT OF THE URINE TEST SHOWS TRACES OF DYSPEPSIA POWDER, IRON –
TABLETS, HEART AND LIVER PILLS AND DENTURE CREAM. PRETTY DAMNING STUFF EH?

TITLES BY

POWERFRESH
. NORTHAMPTON . ENGLAND .

CRINKLED 'N' WRINKLED	MAD TO PLAY GOLF...
TRUE LOVE	MAD TO HAVE A BABY...
OH NO IT'S XMAS AGAIN	MAD TO GET MARRIED...
ITS NO FUN BEING A MOTHER	MAD TO HAVE A PONY
FUNNY SIDE OF 30s	MAD TO HAVE A CAT
FUNNY SIDE OF 40 HIM	MAD TO HAVE A COMPUTER
FUNNY SIDE OF 40 HER	YOU DON'T HAVE TO BE MAD TO BE 40 HIM
FUNNY SIDE OF 50 HIM	YOU DON'T HAVE TO BE MAD TO BE 40 HER
FUNNY SIDE OF 50 HER	YOU DON'T HAVE TO BE MAD TO BE 50 HIM
FUNNY SIDE OF 60'S	YOU DON'T HAVE TO BE MAD TO BE 50 HER
FUNNY SIDE OF SEX	MAD ON FOOTBALL
FLYING FUNNIES	MAD TO BE A MOTHER
GOLFAHOLICS	MAD TO BE A FATHER
MIDLIFE CRISIS	LOVE & PASSION FOR THE ELDERLY
WE'RE GETTING MARRIED	SPORTS FOR THE ELDERLY
THE DEFINITIVE GUIDE TO VASECTOMY	GOOD WHILE IT LASTED
KEEP FIT WITH YOUR CAT	A BABY BOOK
HORNY MAN'S ADULT DOODLE BOOK	FUNNY FARM SILLY MOOS
HORNY GIRL'S ADULT DOODLE BOOK	FUNNY FARMS PIGGERY JOKERY
IF BABIES COULD TALK	FUNNY FARM SHEEP & NASTY
CAT CRAZY	DICKS NAUGHTY BOOK
THE BARE BOTTOM BOOK	HOW TO SCORE
MAD TO TRAVEL BY AIR...	VIVA VIRILITY

For more information on these or other titles please write to :
Powerfresh Ltd. 3 Gray Street, Northampton, NN1 3QQ, ENGLAND.
Telephone 01604 630 996 Fax 01604 621 013
E Mail pwrfresh@ nccnet.co.uk